No. 6

Changes in the Cumbrian countryside

First report of the National
Countryside Monitoring Scheme

Further copies of this report can be obtained from
Interpretive Services Branch, Nature Conservancy Council
Northminster House, Peterborough PE1 1UA

Research and survey in nature conservation series

No. 1   The use of permanent quadrats to record changes in the structure and composition of Wytham Woods, Oxfordshire. A S Horsfall and K J Kirby. 1985. £1.00.

No. 2   Monitoring the abundance of butterflies 1976-1985. E Pollard, M L Hall and T J Bibby. 1986. £6.50.

No. 3   Saltmarsh survey of Great Britain: Bibliography. Compiled by Kevin Charman, Wanda Fojt and Shirley Penny. 1986. £2.00.

No. 4   A survey of the numbers and breeding distribution of the North Atlantic gannet Sula bassana and an assessment of the changes which have occurred since Operation Seafarer 1969/70. Sarah Wanless. 1987. £3.00.

No. 5   Agricultural structures policy and nature conservation in Upland Grampian: a pilot study. J R Crabtree, Sue Evans, Brian J Revell and Philip M K Leat. 1987. £2.00.

No. 6   Changes in the Cumbrian countryside. First report of the National Countryside Monitoring Scheme. 1987. £3.50.

The principal contributors to this report were Jonathan Budd, Philip Oswald and Peter Welsh, and the report was based on data collected and analysed by Hilary Anderson and Anne Messer.

Contents

Preface

For a quarter of a century the Nature Conservancy Council and others have carried out various survey and monitoring projects relevant to nature conservation, but most of these have related to particular sites or to species or groups of plants or animals rather than to the countryside at large. The National Countryside Monitoring Scheme (NCMS) was set up to fill this gap, by providing data on the distribution and extent of the various structural components or features of the countryside and on the changes that have occurred to them since the Second World War. Never before has an attempt been made to measure the extent and change of wildlife habitats in detail on a national scale.

Such a major undertaking could only be based on a sample survey, and aerial photographs are the only consistent source of data over the time span that is involved. The sampling had to be stratified to take account of regional and altitudinal variation in land-use; it was therefore decided to base the study on counties (or districts in Scotland) and on three levels or "land types" within each area treated. An automated data-processing system was required to handle the large quantities of information, and this involved photogrammetric plotting, digital mapping and statistical analysis. Substantial difficulties had to be overcome in assembling suitable hardware and software for the project.

Cumbria was chosen as the first county to survey, and it gives me great pleasure to introduce this report of the methods adopted, the principal findings and the implications for nature conservation of the changes in the Cumbrian countryside between the 1940s and the 1970s. Estimated rates of change over the last decade are discussed in a supplement.

For the future, we are extending the scheme throughout Great Britain in order to establish baselines for further monitoring of countryside change, using, we hope, the developing technology of remote sensing in addition to aerial photography.

Dr Derek Langslow
Assistant Chief Scientist

Summary

Changes in the extent of almost thirty kinds of countryside features which have occurred between the 1940s and 1970s in Cumbria have been estimated from a stratified random sample of aerial photographs within three categories of land type – Lowland, Intermediate and Upland.

The magnitude of net change was fairly consistent throughout the county, but the sorts of changes varied considerably from one area to another. At least a third of the county underwent change of some kind, and more change was recorded in lowland and intermediate than in upland areas. The last category, however, showed change within 23% of its area – a large change in what is normally considered to be a relatively stable environment. All three possible types of change were observed. These are:

i.   changes which are virtually without any compensatory change elsewhere and so produce a correspondingly large net gain or loss;

ii.   changes, sometimes extensive, but including both gains and losses, so that the overall result is a small net shift;

iii.   minimal alterations in the extent of quite stable features, producing insignificant overall change.

Over 100 km^2 of semi-natural broadleaved woods have been lost since the 1940s; this means that nearly half of the woodland of this kind in the 1940s had become something else by the 1970s. The majority of this loss was in the lowlands. Here they have been replaced mainly by improved grassland, scrub, mixed woodland and conifer plantations. Though there have been gains of broadleaved woodland on other sites, these new woods have much lower nature conservation value than the mature woods which have been lost. Of other woodland types, coniferous plantation showed the greatest change, increasing in extent so as to cover an area over twice that occupied in the 1940s. Most of this increase was at the expense of semi-natural habitats such as unimproved grassland and dwarf shrub heath (heather and similar vegetation).

Grassland habitats comprised 62% of the surface area of Cumbria in the 1940s and the same coverage was observed for the 1970s. Although this suggests great stability, in fact there were gains and losses, each of some 1,200 km^2. Gains occurred throughout the county, but particularly in improved grassland in the lowlands and in unimproved grassland within the uplands. Losses have been concentrated in the lowland and intermediate areas, mainly through improvement of unimproved grassland or loss of improved grassland to arable use.

Arable land has shown significant gains, mostly from grassland, but these have been largely counterbalanced by losses of arable land to grassland, resulting in little overall change.

Dwarf shrub heath has shown an overall 70% loss to a number of other features. By far the greatest decline has been, perhaps not surprisingly, in the uplands.

Built-up areas have shown a 43% net increase, and by far the largest part of this has occurred, understandably, in the lowlands.

Estimates have also been made of change in two linear features – hedgerows and treelines. These too have shown considerable change. For example, over 9,000 km of hedgerows have been lost and, although some new hedges have been planted, these, like the new broadleaved woodland, are not yet as valuable in terms of nature conservation as those which have been removed. There has also been an overall loss in treelines, but this has been smaller (8%).

The significance for nature conservation of the changes observed between the 1940s and the 1970s is not necessarily related directly to their magnitude or even to the actual area covered by each kind of feature. Certain kinds of features have undergone large changes, but these may be ecologically less significant than smaller changes in more valuable wildlife habitats.

Most of the losses in Cumbria have occurred in semi-natural habitats, while the corresponding gains have been to man-made features normally of lower value for wildlife. Even when kinds of features that can be classified as semi-natural have shown gains, these acquisitions do not yet support the mature floras and faunas that have been lost elsewhere.

Aerial photographic coverage for the 1980s is insufficient to provide equivalent data for full comparisons with the position in the 1940s and the 1970s, but it has proved possible to estimate annual rates of change for some of the principal features from about a third of the area used for the main study. The results, presented in a supplement, suggest that the trends observed in the main study have generally persisted over the last decade.

1   Introduction

The passage through Parliament of the Wildlife and Countryside Bill and the continuing debate engendered by the ensuing Act of 1981 have increased public concern about the ways in which the structure and appearance of the countryside have been, and may in future be, affected by changes in farming, forestry and other land-uses. Much of the concern has focussed on changes since the Second World War related to fiscal and strategic policies to increase farm output and the nation's timber reserves. Intensified husbandry and economies of scale, made possible by improvements in farming and forestry technology, have made substantial impacts on rural land management and infrastructure.

Large-block conifer afforestation and the conversion of semi-natural grassland, moorland, heathland, native woodland and wetland into arable land and short-term grassland have altered, and also simplified, much of the rural landscape. Surveys by the Nature Conservancy Council have shown that the changes differ in kind and extent between different parts of Great Britain. However, comparisons both between wildlife habitats and between geographical areas have been hampered by differences in survey methods and comprehensiveness. Large parts of the country have not been surveyed at all.

Accordingly, the NCC has begun a survey of change in countryside features throughout Great Britain, in a manner which permits local as well as general trends to be identified. The aim is to obtain comprehensive data for all parts of the country. This is being done on a standard basis so that different areas and features may be compared, using methods which will withstand critical examination.

The information obtained will be relevant for assessing the effects of past, present and future countryside policies, and the NCC expects that it will be of value to a wide range of agencies with interests and responsibilities in the rural environment.

1.1   Objectives

The objectives of the National Countryside Monitoring Scheme are to establish a standard, technically robust system for providing quantitative data on the distribution and extent of defined structural components of the rural landscape during the 1940s and as near to the present day as possible so as to be able to estimate the changes that have occurred over this period of time.

1.2   The countryside features to be measured

From the conservation point of view, the natural and semi-natural wildlife habitats are the most important features to measure. The aim of this survey is thus to provide as much information about these habitats and the changes they have undergone as possible. The amount and quality of data that can be collected depend on the data sources available.

1.3   Data sources

The data sources used must provide:

a.   data capable of expression on a standard basis;

9

b.   high and specifiable accuracy of identification and measurement for each feature for which separate data are obtained at each study locality;

c.   coverage complete enough to be representative of the times and geographical units to which they apply.

The data sources must therefore be free from initial bias or capable of correction to allow for known biases where these exist.

Of the several potentially usable data sources, some are not capable of distinguishing adequately between certain of the features for which data are required. Among potential sources in this category are Ordnance Survey and other maps and (at their present state of development) remote-sensing systems such as Landsat and radar. Only the use of standard black and white vertical aerial photography is capable of satisfying the requirements retrospectively to the 1940s.

The kinds of features that can be identified from aerial photographs are listed in Annex 1 and defined in Annex 2. Not all types exist in every geographical unit, nor is every type always accurately distinguishable from every other related type. Accordingly, for some geographical units, the list of features will be shorter and, if necessary, less detailed than for others. The list in Annex 1 is structured hierarchically to allow recording of combined groups of features when appropriate. These features can be related to the National Vegetation Classification, which is being developed at the University of Lancaster under a contract with the NCC and will be published by Cambridge University Press.

1.4   Design of a sample-based project

Cost and time preclude a study based on complete coverage of the country, but adequate information can be obtained from statistical inference derived from random samples. The project is therefore sample-based, with the sampling strategy designed so that statistical rigour is preserved. The principal criterion is that, at least for those features indicated by an asterisk in Annex 1, net changes of 10% or more in extent should be detected with 95% confidence. No attempt is being made to assimilate data from other sources, which are likely to be incompatible and so to prejudice the results. Technical aspects of the project methods are discussed in the appendix (pp. 26-29).

Different parts of Britain vary greatly in kinds of land and land-use. Features may be abundant in one region but scarce or absent in others and can vary in occurrence and extent even between similar geographical areas. Absolute and relative amounts of change can differ in a similar way. In order to allow for these variations the study is stratified on a county basis (district in Scotland). Sampling intensity has to be increased as heterogeneity rises, so that statistical precision is maintained.

Variability also exists within counties (or districts). Such variation has similar implications for sampling intensity within counties as between counties; hence the sampling has been further stratified into three broad land types - Upland, Lowland and Intermediate. The stratification helps explain some of the variability between samples, thus increasing the accuracy of the final estimates. A county (or district) is stratified into the three broad land types by amalgamating the land classes of the classification system developed by the Institute of Terrestrial Ecology (ITE). Each of its land classes is defined according to physical geography and land-use.

10

First, the total area covered by each of the kinds of features sampled within each land class is estimated, and the results are weighted according to the relative abundance of each land class in each broad land type. The weighted estimates are then combined to provide overall estimates for each land type and for the whole county.

2   The monitoring project for Cumbria

The previous sections briefly describe the context, objectives and design of the NCMS. The following sections examine how the techniques were applied to the county of Cumbria.

2.1   Sampling

The first step in the sampling procedure was the stratification of the county. The basis for the stratification was the ITE's land classes produced for Cumbria by Bunce & Smith (1978), who assigned each 1 x 1 km square to one of 16 land classes. For this project these land classes were grouped into the three broad land types (Lowland, Intermediate and Upland). Bunce & Smith also included a series of coastal land classes, but, because this project is not designed to sample features confined to the coastal belt, these classes are here either omitted or else included in the Lowland land type.

Figure 1 shows the classification of the 1 x 1 km squares into the three broad land types and the coastal classes. To ensure adequate sampling of each of the three types it was also necessary to stratify the 5 x 5 km squares. Each 5 x 5 km square was allocated to a land type on the basis of the land type to which the most 1 x 1 km squares within it had been assigned. The resulting stratification is shown in Figure 2. It was then possible to select the sample squares randomly.

Work done by Langdale-Brown et al. (1980) suggested that a 10% sample was sufficient to achieve the required accuracy for the results. For Cumbria it was initially decided to select a 20% sample to allow for the greater heterogeneity of the habitats in the county. However, a 10% sample was found to be sufficient to reduce the standard errors to the required level (see Section 1.4). Figure 3 shows the sample 5 x 5 km squares randomly selected for Cumbria.

2.2   Aerial photography

Ideally, complete air-photo cover is required for unbiased selection of samples. A detailed search of the air-photo records for Cumbria was made and a directory of air-photo cover was produced for the county (Anderson & Budd 1984). Two periods of extensive cover were found. Between 1970 and 1976 the Ordnance Survey photographed the whole county. The photography was of good quality and varied in scale from 1:22,000 to 1:26,000. The other period was 1945-1949, when the Royal Air Force photographed the county at scales between 1:27,500 and 1:32,000, though most of the photographs were at a scale of 1:28,000. Unfortunately a strip across the centre of the county, amounting to approximately 10% of its area, was not covered in this set. Any potential bias caused by this gap in cover is reduced by the stratification of the county. Some additional photographs were found for 1983. These had been taken by the Ministry of Agriculture, Fisheries and Food at a scale of 1:11,000 during August of that year. Copies were purchased as aids to interpretation of the earlier photographs and checking in the field.

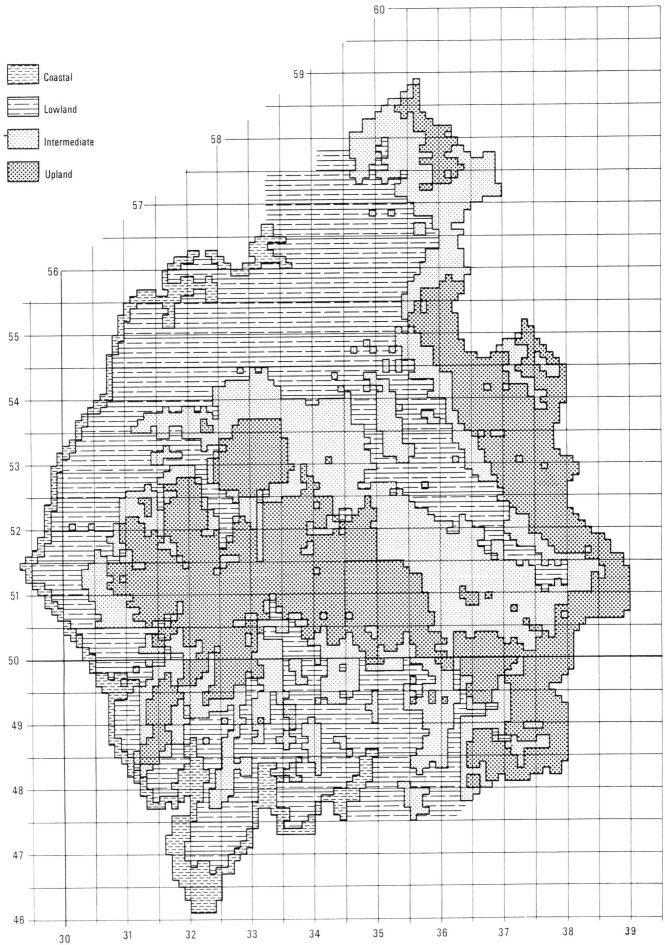

Figure 1   Stratification of the 1 x 1 km squares of the National Grid in Cumbria into three broad land types - Lowland, Intermediate and Upland - and coastal land classes (treated as Lowland)

12

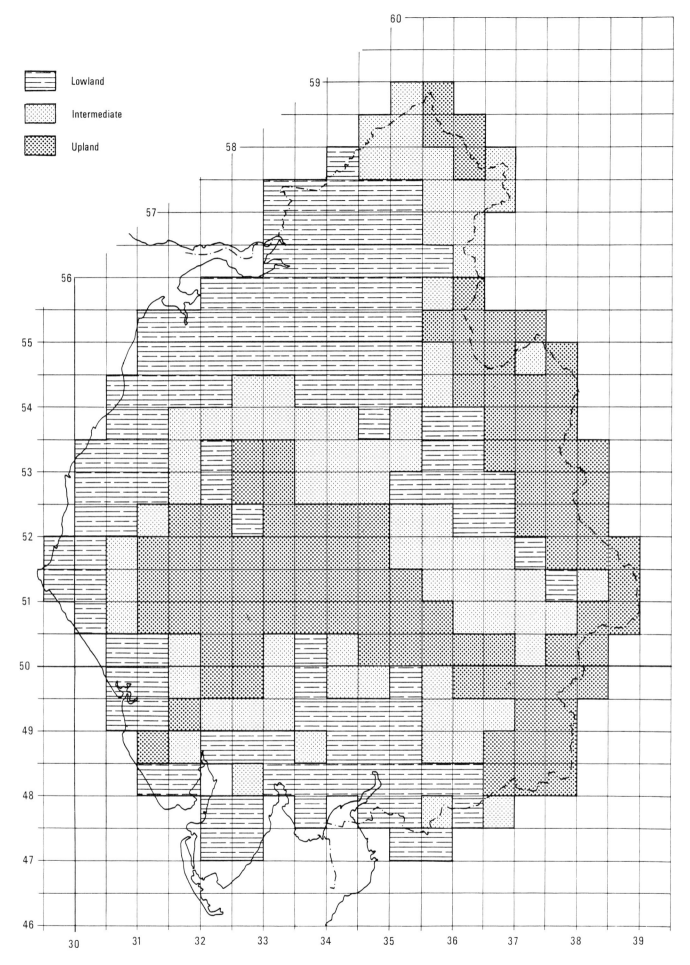

Figure 2   Stratification of the 5 x 5 km squares of the National Grid in Cumbria
into three broad land types – Lowland, Intermediate and Upland

13

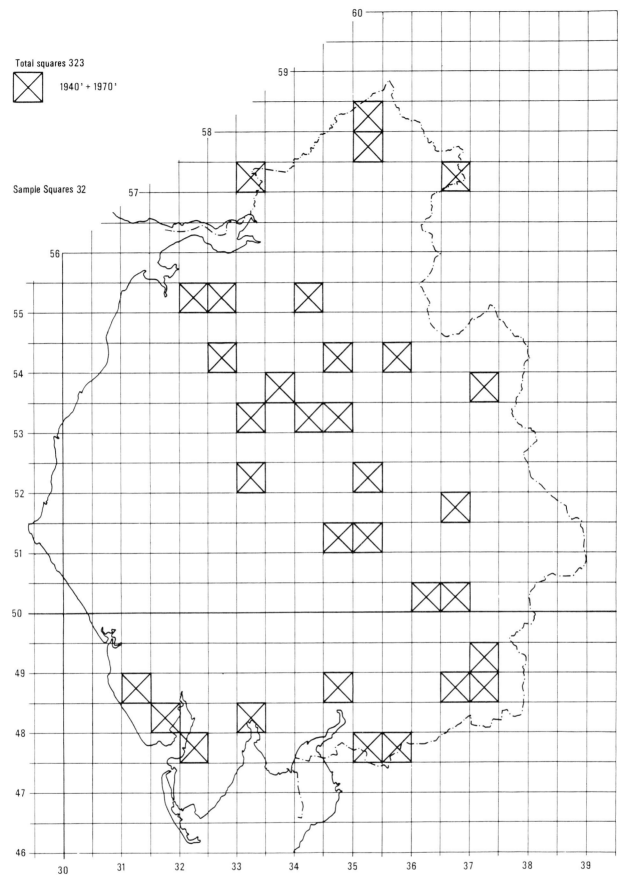

Figure 3   5 x 5 km squares of the National Grid in Cumbria selected as a 10% stratified random sample to assess changes in countryside features between the 1940s and the 1970s

14

2.3   Photo-interpretation

Most of the features described in Annex 1 (see Section 1.3) were readily identified on the aerial photographs.   Young plantation, wet ground and semi-improved grassland were added to this list as a result of the work done in Cumbria.   The category of semi-improved grassland was introduced to reduce the problems of defining boundaries between unimproved and improved grassland.   For example, a field may have tonal and textural characteristics found in both types of grassland; it is then simpler to classify the field as semi-improved grassland.

Problems were also encountered in distinguishing between the improved grassland and arable features.   The main reason for this was the high proportion of the aerial photographs taken in June, when it is extremely difficult to distinguish between them.   On the other hand, the summer months are best for the interpretation of the woodland features.   Some of the early photographs were taken in winter, making it difficult to identify the presence of broadleaved woodlands. This problem also applied to treelines. Cross-checking with the more recent photographs helped to overcome it.

It was not possible to distinguish consistently between broadleaved or mixed plantation and the corresponding semi-natural features, so the results for these must be treated with caution.   The felled woodland category has proved very difficult to identify, and in Cumbria few clear examples of felling were found, though some felled areas may have been classified as scrub.   Usually, for a felled area to be identified correctly, the felling must have occurred within a year before the aerial photographs were taken.

In the uplands, where few man-made boundaries exist, problems were encountered in defining vegetation boundaries. This was a result of the interpreter's having to define a line subjectively through the zone of change between two features where no distinct boundary exists.   It is thus unlikely that the interpreter will choose exactly the same boundary for the second time period. Care was taken to identify areas where this problem occurred and to disregard any apparent changes shown by the maps.

It is helpful to examine the two sets of photographs together because evidence on one set may assist the interpretation of what would otherwise be ambiguous features on the other. It was essential to make field visits to each sample square to survey the areas where it had not been possible to identify a feature with certainty from the aerial photography alone and also in order to assess the overall accuracy of interpretation.   These field checks were applied both to the early and to the more recent sets of photographs. It even proved possible to find evidence still surviving in the field to assist in the interpretation of the early photographs.

2.4   Data capture and processing

The Kern PG2-L photogrammetric plotting machine (see Appendix, Section 8) proved ideal for the interpretation and mapping processes, and the fact that it could do both at once saved much time.   The high-quality stereoscopic image and the eightfold magnification helped considerably with the interpretation of the aerial photographs. The accuracy of the data about features was well within the limits required, even though some of the air-photo negatives had been damaged.

Digital data were recorded simultaneously with the production of the map plotted by the pantograph. The data for each square were stored on floppy disks. This data file was then processed through a series of computer programs in order to calculate the areas of the various kinds of features. At the time of the Cumbria study this was the limit of digital mapping software. Thus the preparation of the data for the statistical programs had to be done manually.

A third map was produced for each sample square showing the changes in features. This was done by superimposing the earlier and the more recent maps. Most of the resulting areas shared boundaries with the original areas shown on the first two maps. Figure 4 is part of one of the resultant maps, including a section of the M6 motorway. Linear measurements were recorded manually by using a map measurer. All the line and area data were recorded on data forms ready for subsequent statistical analysis on the mainframe computer at the Unit of Statistics of the Agricultural and Food Research Council at the University of Edinburgh.

3   **Results**

3.1   Estimated areas of features

Estimates of area for each feature for the 1940s (1945-49) and 1970s (1970-76) are shown in Tables 1-4. These estimates are calculated by multiplying up the results of sampled areas, using the area covered by each kind of feature within each ITE land class (see Sections 1.4 and 2.1). The results are presented as total estimates for the county in Table 1 and for the three broad land types (Lowland, Intermediate and Upland) in Tables 2-4.

Grassland is the dominant group of features, covering about 62% of the county both in the 1940s and in the 1970s (see Table 1). Next in extent are the moorland habitats (mire and heath), covering 18% of the county in the 1940s but reduced to 12% by the 1970s. Most of this decrease has been due to losses of heather (dwarf shrub heath), 70% of which has gone since the 1940s. At the other extreme, coniferous plantation has shown the largest gain, 127%. In both these cases the change has been in one direction, a loss or a gain. Grassland, on the other hand, has undergone more complex changes, with substantial gains and losses resulting in a small net change. It is important to distinguish between a small overall change of this kind and a small net change in a feature such as cliffs, where there have in fact been few losses or gains during the study period.

Estimates of extent and of gains and losses of each feature within each of the three land types are shown in Tables 2-4. Many of the features and changes are associated with particular land types. It should be noted that it is not only the estimates of extent that show these geographical differences: estimates of change over the 30-year period also vary from one land type to another.

Within the Lowland land type (Table 2) there are four wildlife habitats that have undergone large percentage losses. Lowland dwarf shrub heath has suffered a 59.5% net loss and unimproved grassland a 48.5% net loss. The greatest actual loss of broadleaved woodland (64.5 km² or nearly half) has occurred within the Lowland land type, but the percentage net loss appears as only 19.2% owing mainly to the growth of new woodland but perhaps also partly to mistaken inclusion of some broadleaved plantations; this is lower than in the Upland land

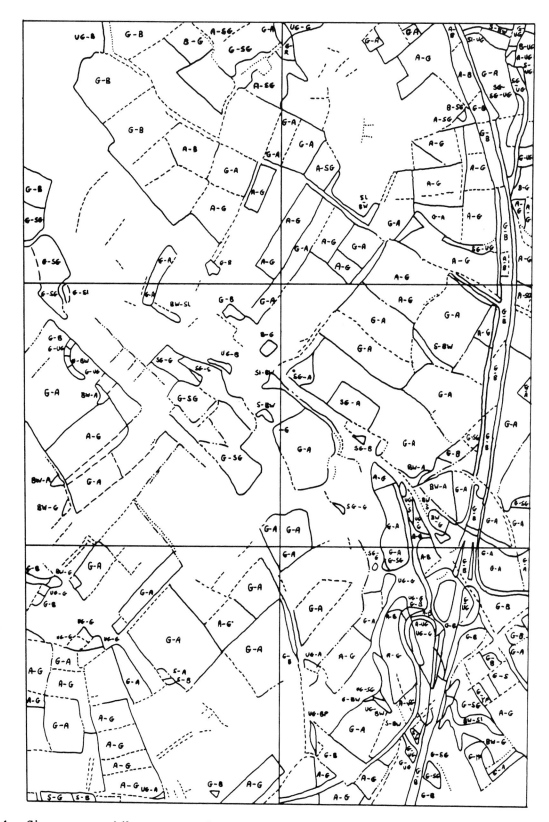

Figure 4   Six square kilometres of Cumbria, showing changes in countryside features between 1949 and 1971

The abbreviations in each area where change has occurred indicate the 1949 and 1971 features. Broken lines indicate changed linear features (see Section 3.3).

17

Table 1

Estimates of extent and change in square kilometres for the features in the county of Cumbria (total area 6689 square kilometres) from the 1940s to the 1970s

Features	1940s	1970s	Increase	Decrease	Net change	% net change
Broadleaved woodland	219.5*	183.8*	69.3*	105.0*	-35.7*	-16.3*
Broadleaved plantation	0.0	0.1	0.1	0.0	0.1	0.0
Coniferous woodland	0.3	0.0	0.0	0.3	-0.3	-100.0
Coniferous plantation	51.7*	117.2*	81.6*	16.1*	65.6	126.9
Mixed woodland	26.8*	57.8*	41.8*	10.8*	31.1*	116.0*
Young plantation	26.7*	45.7*	39.8*	20.8	19.0	71.2
Felled woodland	0.0	0.7	0.7	0.0	0.7	0.0
Parkland	12.1*	17.2*	9.5*	4.4*	5.0*	41.5
Scrub, tall	27.4*	26.4*	14.6*	15.6*	-1.0	-3.7
Scrub, low	86.6*	114.0*	86.0*	58.6*	27.3*	31.5*
Bracken	98.9*	164.6*	94.3*	28.6*	65.6*	66.3*
Dwarf shrub heath, lowland	116.3*	33.8*	4.2*	86.7*	-82.5*	-71.0*
Dwarf shrub heath, moorland	298.5*	89.5*	1.6	210.5*	-209.0*	-70.0*
Blanket mire	617.5*	540.7*	0.9	77.8*	-76.9*	-12.5*
Lowland raised mire	143.7*	116.6*	0.0	27.1	-27.1	-18.9
Wet ground	14.1*	15.8*	11.9*	10.2*	1.7	12.4
Marginal inundation	0.7	0.8	0.2	0.1	0.1	15.0
Standing natural water	29.8	29.1	0.0	0.7*	-0.7	-2.3
Standing man-made water	4.1	3.1	0.1	1.0	-0.9	-21.9
Running natural water	12.6*	12.6*	0.0	0.0	0.0	0.0
Running canalised water	0.5	0.5	0.0	0.0	0.0	0.0
Unimproved grassland	1325.4*	1362.2*	387.4*	350.6*	36.8	2.8
Semi-improved grassland	395.8*	448.8*	279.9*	226.9*	53.1	13.4
Improved grassland	2419.4*	2348.0*	552.7*	624.1*	-71.4	-3.0
Arable	580.1*	704.6*	428.8*	304.3*	124.5*	21.5*
Cliff	17.2*	17.9*	1.4*	0.7	0.7	3.9
Quarry	6.1*	13.1*	8.0*	0.9	7.1*	118.3*
Bare ground	2.1	2.4	0.4	0.1	0.3	72.4
Built land	155.2*	221.9*	71.7*	5.0*	66.8*	43.0*

Estimates are given to the nearest decimal place.

* Estimated with 95% confidence.

Table 2

Estimates of extent and change in square kilometres for features in the Lowland land type (total area 2717 square kilometres) within the county of Cumbria from the 1940s to the 1970s

Features	1940s	1970s	Increase	Decrease	Net change	% net change
Broadleaved woodland	130.4*	105.4*	39.5*	64.5*	-25.0*	-19.2*
Broadleaved plantation	0.0	0.1	0.1	0.0	0.1	0.0
Coniferous woodland	0.0	0.0	0.0	0.0	0.0	0.0
Coniferous plantation	11.9*	20.1*	13.8*	5.5*	8.3*	69.7*
Mixed woodland	17.0*	42.1*	34.1*	9.0*	25.1	148.0
Young plantation	5.8*	20.5*	17.6*	2.9*	14.7*	251.2
Felled woodland	0.0	0.7	0.7	0.0	0.7	0.0
Parkland	6.5	9.6*	4.4*	1.3*	3.1	47.8
Scrub, tall	12.9*	14.1	7.3	6.1*	1.2	9.4
Scrub, low	51.4*	64.8*	48.6*	35.2*	13.4	26.1
Bracken	25.0*	53.8*	36.5*	7.6*	28.9	115.6
Dwarf shrub heath, lowland	31.5	12.8	3.6	22.3*	-18.7*	-59.5*
Dwarf shrub heath, moorland	2.6	0.0	0.0	2.6	-2.6	-98.3
Blanket mire	1.9	1.9	0.0	0.0	0.0	0.0
Lowland raised mire	79.9	70.4	0.0	9.5	-9.5	-11.9
Wet ground	0.2	0.3	0.2	0.1	0.1	81.2
Marginal inundation	0.2	0.2	0.1	0.1	0.0	18.5
Standing natural water	1.9*	1.6*	0.0	0.3	-0.3	-14.7
Standing man-made water	1.8	1.5	0.1	0.4	-0.3	-17.9
Running natural water	5.1*	5.1*	0.0	0.0	0.0	0.0
Running canalised water	0.4	0.4	0.0	0.0	0.0	0.0
Unimproved grassland	174.2*	89.7*	29.6*	114.1*	-84.5*	-48.5*
Semi-improved grassland	129.6*	129.5*	90.0*	90.1*	-0.1	-0.1
Improved grassland	1484.3*	1411.3*	330.8*	403.7*	-72.9	-4.9
Arable	425.4*	480.0*	286.1*	231.5*	54.7	12.9
Cliff	0.0	0.0	0.0	0.0	0.0	0.0
Quarry	2.9*	7.8*	5.5*	0.6	4.9*	168.1*
Bare ground	1.8	2.0	0.2	0.0	0.2	359.0
Built land	112.4*	171.2*	61.6*	2.9*	58.7*	52.2*

Estimates are given to the nearest decimal place.

* Estimated with 95% confidence.

19

Table 3

Estimates of extent and change in square kilometres for features in the Intermediate land type (total area 2003 square kilometres) within the county of Cumbria from the 1940s to the 1970s

Features	1940s	1970s	Increase	Decrease	Net change	% net change
Broadleaved woodland	71.6*	65.2*	27.0*	33.5*	-6.4	-9.0
Broadleaved plantation	0.0	0.0	0.0	0.0	0.0	0.0
Coniferous woodland	0.3*	0.0	0.0	0.3*	-0.3	-100.0
Coniferous plantation	39.2*	94.2	65.5	10.6*	55.0	140.1
Mixed woodland	9.1*	14.1*	6.8*	1.7*	5.1*	55.6*
Young plantation	19.5	22.1*	19.6*	17.1	2.5	13.0
Felled woodland	0.0	0.0	0.0	0.0	0.0	0.0
Parkland	5.6	6.7	4.1	3.0	1.1	19.9
Scrub, tall	10.0*	8.6*	5.9*	7.3*	-1.4	-14.1
Scrub, low	27.0*	33.5*	24.8*	18.3*	6.4	23.9
Bracken	25.5	42.8*	24.4*	7.1	17.4	68.1
Dwarf shrub heath, lowland	75.5*	19.6	0.4*	56.3*	-56.0*	-74.1*
Dwarf shrub heath, moorland	39.2	19.0	1.3	21.4	-20.2	-51.5
Blanket mire	21.5	17.1	0.0	4.3	-4.3	-20.2
Lowland raised mire	50.6	33.0	0.0	17.5	-17.5	-34.7
Wet ground	5.9*	6.4*	4.2*	3.7*	0.5	9.0
Marginal inundation	0.3*	0.4*	0.1	0.0	0.1	14.0
Standing natural water	1.7*	1.4	0.0	0.4*	-0.4	-22.2
Standing man-made water	2.3	1.7	0.0	0.6	-0.6	-27.0
Running natural water	5.9*	5.9*	0.0	0.0	0.0	0.0
Running canalised water	0.0	0.0	0.0	0.0	0.0	0.0
Unimproved grassland	349.6*	292.7*	80.4*	137.3*	-56.9*	-16.3*
Semi-improved grassland	189.5*	192.6*	112.1*	108.9*	3.1	1.7
Improved grassland	856.0*	854.1*	202.4*	204.3*	-1.9	-0.2
Arable	154.3*	220.6*	139.1*	72.8*	66.3*	43.0*
Cliff	0.4*	0.2	0.1	0.3	-0.2	-45.2
Quarry	2.0*	3.6	1.8	0.2	1.6	79.4
Bare ground	0.1	0.1	0.0	0.0	0.0	0.0
Built land	40.4*	47.3*	9.0*	2.1*	7.0*	17.2*

Estimates are given to the nearest decimal place.

* Estimated with 95% confidence.

Table 4

Estimates of extent and change in square kilometres for features in the Upland land type
(total area 1969 square kilometres) within the county of Cumbria from the 1940s to the 1970s

Features	1940s	1970s	Increase	Decrease	Net change	% net change
Broadleaved woodland	17.6*	13.3*	2.8*	7.1*	-4.3*	-24.5*
Broadleaved plantation	0.0	0.0	0.0	0.0	0.0	0.0
Coniferous woodland	0.0	0.0	0.0	0.0	0.0	0.0
Coniferous plantation	0.6	2.9	2.3	0.0	2.3	390.5
Mixed woodland	0.7*	1.6	1.0	0.1	0.9	127.1
Young plantation	1.3*	3.1*	2.7*	0.9	1.8*	135.3*
Felled woodland	0.0	0.0	0.0	0.0	0.0	0.0
Parkland	0.1	0.9*	0.9*	0.1	0.8*	825.2*
Scrub, tall	4.4*	3.6*	1.4*	2.2*	-0.8	-18.5
Scrub, low	8.2*	15.7*	12.5*	5.0*	7.5*	90.9*
Bracken	48.5*	67.9*	33.3*	13.9*	19.4	40.0
Dwarf shrub heath, lowland	9.3	1.5*	0.3*	8.1	-7.8	-84.0
Dwarf shrub heath, moorland	256.7*	70.5*	0.3	186.5*	-186.2*	-72.5*
Blanket mire	594.2*	521.6*	0.9	73.4*	-72.5*	-12.2*
Lowland raised mire	13.1	13.1	0.0	0.0	0.0	0.0
Wet ground	8.0*	9.2*	7.4*	6.3*	1.1	13.7
Marginal inundation	0.2	0.2	0.0	0.0	0.0	0.0
Standing natural water	26.2	26.2	0.0	0.0	0.0	0.0
Standing man-made water	0.0	0.0	0.0	0.0	0.0	0.0
Running natural water	1.6*	1.6*	0.0	0.0	0.0	0.0
Running canalised water	0.1	0.1	0.0	0.0	0.0	0.0
Unimproved grassland	801.5*	979.7*	277.4*	99.2*	178.2*	22.2*
Semi-improved grassland	76.7*	126.7*	77.9*	27.8*	50.0	65.3
Improved grassland	79.1*	82.5*	19.5*	16.1*	3.4	4.3
Arable	0.4*	4.0*	3.7	0.1	3.6	856.7
Cliff	16.8*	17.6*	1.2*	0.4	0.8	4.9
Quarry	1.1*	1.8*	0.7*	0.1	0.6	56.2
Bare ground	0.2	0.3*	0.2	0.1	0.1	36.1
Built land	2.3*	3.4*	1.1*	0.0	1.1*	46.9*

Estimates are given to the nearest decimal place.

* Estimated with 95% confidence.

21

type, where a much smaller area of such woodland has shown a 24.5% decrease. Lowland raised mire has undergone a loss of 11.9%. The Lowland land type has seen very large net gains in coniferous plantation, mixed woodland and young plantation - 69.7%, 148.0% and 251.2% respectively.

In the Intermediate land type (Table 3) no one feature predominates. The most significant difference between this land type and the other two is the proportion of coniferous plantation. Over 80% (94.2 km^2) of the county estimate for this habitat in the 1970s occurs within the Intermediate land type. This is an increase of 140% since the 1940s. There have also been large increases in mixed woodland, bracken and arable, the last having a larger percentage increase (43%) than in the Lowland land type(12.9%). Most of the losses have occurred within the moorland (mire and heath) habitats.

Within the Upland land type (Table 4) two groups of habitats predominate. Unimproved grassland and the moorland habitats together cover over 80% of this land type. Since many of the other features have little cover, estimates of change can appear extreme. For example, arable shows nearly a 900% increase but this represents a net change of only 3.6 km^2. Such figures are misleading and thus not as important as they may at first appear. The moorland habitats again show large losses, with over 186 km^2 of moorland dwarf shrub heath alone being lost. Unimproved grassland shows a 22.2% net increase, which contrasts with the net losses in the other two land types. This is due to gains from the moorland habitats, whereas in the other land types unimproved grassland was lost to improved grassland and arable. An even greater increase (65.3%) is shown by the semi-improved grassland.

3.2   Interchange between features

Tables 1-4 provide the estimates of area for each feature and the gains and losses that have occurred; they do not, however, show how these changes have taken place. Table 5 is an interchange matrix for the whole county. The features have been summarised into 17 groups in order to reduce the size of the matrix. The diagonal values in bold type, for example 114.5 km^2 for Broad/Broad (= broadleaved woodland), represent the area of each group that has not changed during the study period. The vertical columns show the losses from the group at the head of each column to the groups listed on the left. In the case of broadleaved woodland, these have been principally to coniferous woodland (10.8 km^2), mixed woodland (25.9 km^2), scrub (18.5 km^2) and improved grassland (23.0 km^2). Gains are shown in the horizontal rows, and for broadleaved woodland these have been principally from scrub (27.6 km^2) but also from dwarf shrub heath (10.4 km^2) and improved grassland (10.1 km^2).

Table 6 summarises the changes of more than 10 km^2 from one kind of feature to another for the whole county, with a breakdown of them between the three broad land types. Once again, significant geographical differences can be seen. The largest single change in both the Lowland and the Intermediate land types has been from improved grassland to arable. There has, however, been a considerable amount of change between these two features in both directions owing to crop rotation. By far the biggest change in the Upland land type is from moorland dwarf shrub heath to unimproved grassland, 171.3 km^2 in all, with the change from blanket mire to unimproved grassland second at 71.6 km^2.

22

Table 5

Estimates of gains and losses between features in Cumbria from the 1940s to the 1970s (square kilometres)

	Losses																	Totals 1970s
	Broad	Conif	Mixed	Park	Scrub	Brack	Heath	Mire	Minund	Swater	Rwater	Ugrass	Sgrass	Igrass	Arable	Baregr	Built	
Broad	**114.5**	2.9	6.4	0.2	27.6	0.2	10.4	1.0	0.0	0.0	0.0	7.3	2.4	10.1	0.2	0.0	0.8	183.9
Conif	10.8	**57.4**	1.5	0.4	5.6	0.3	20.0	4.3	0.0	0.0	0.0	30.2	13.3	18.2	0.5	0.0	0.2	162.9
Mixed	25.9	3.0	**16.0**	0.2	2.8	0.5	2.3	0.7	0.0	0.0	0.0	4.0	1.1	1.3	0.2	0.1	0.0	57.8
Park	3.0	0.0	0.1	**7.7**	1.8	0.0	0.2	0.0	0.0	0.0	0.0	1.1	1.4	1.6	0.2	0.0	0.0	17.2
Scrub	18.5	4.0	0.6	0.5	**43.9**	2.9	6.1	10.8	0.2	0.4	0.0	26.6	9.9	15.0	0.4	0.3	1.0	141.1
Brack	2.9	1.3	0.1	0.0	4.1	**70.3**	10.6	1.3	0.1	0.0	0.0	64.0	6.5	2.8	0.4	0.1	0.1	164.6
G Heath	0.6	0.1	0.4	0.0	0.0	0.0	**117.7**	3.8	0.0	0.0	0.0	0.6	0.0	0.0	0.1	0.1	0.0	123.3
a Mire	0.0	0.0	0.0	0.0	0.0	0.0	0.0	**656.4**	0.0	0.0	0.0	0.6	0.0	0.0	0.0	0.0	0.0	657.3
i Minund	0.1	0.0	0.0	0.0	0.5	0.3	1.0	0.3	**4.5**	0.1	0.0	7.5	1.2	1.1	0.1	0.0	0.0	16.7
n Swater	0.0	0.0	0.0	0.0	0.0	0.0	0.0	0.0	0.0	**32.2**	0.0	0.0	0.0	0.0	0.0	0.0	0.0	32.2
s Rwater	0.0	0.0	0.0	0.0	0.0	0.0	0.0	0.0	0.0	0.0	**13.1**	0.0	0.0	0.0	0.0	0.0	0.0	13.1
Ugrass	6.1	4.5	0.4	0.5	7.7	14.7	208.7	81.1	8.5	0.2	0.0	**974.7**	29.7	22.5	2.2	0.5	0.2	1362.2
Sgrass	6.5	2.2	0.4	0.9	5.9	6.9	23.7	0.6	0.6	0.0	0.0	125.5	**168.9**	99.2	6.9	0.3	0.3	448.8
Igrass	23.0	3.0	0.8	1.7	10.7	0.9	9.2	0.8	0.7	0.3	0.0	71.7	144.9	**1795.3**	282.6	0.0	2.3	2348.0
Arable	2.2	0.0	0.0	0.0	0.8	0.1	1.9	0.0	0.0	0.1	0.0	5.8	10.4	407.2	**275.7**	0.0	0.2	704.6
Baregr	0.4	0.0	0.0	0.0	0.3	1.9	2.2	0.1	0.0	0.0	0.0	2.0	1.6	1.1	0.0	**23.8**	0.0	33.4
Built	5.0	0.2	0.1	0.1	2.4	0.0	0.7	0.0	0.0	0.6	0.0	3.3	4.4	43.8	10.8	0.3	**150.2**	221.9
Totals 1940s	219.5	78.7	26.7	12.1	114.0	98.9	414.8	761.2	14.8	33.9	13.1	1325.4	395.8	2419.4	580.1	25.4	155.2	**6689.0**

Estimates are given to the nearest decimal place.

Abbreviations

Broad:	Semi-natural broadleaved woodland; broadleaved plantation.	**Swater:**	Standing natural water; standing man-made water.
Conif:	Semi-natural coniferous woodland; coniferous plantation; young plantation.	**Rwater:**	Running natural water; running canalised water.
Mixed:	Semi-natural mixed woodland; mixed plantation.	**Ugrass:**	Unimproved grassland.
Park:	Parkland.	**Sgrass:**	Semi-improved grassland.
Scrub:	Scrub, tall; scrub, low; felled woodland.	**Igrass:**	Improved grassland.
Brack:	Bracken.	**Arable:**	Arable.
Heath:	Dwarf shrub heath, lowland; dwarf shrub heath, moorland.	**Baregr:**	Cliff; quarry; bare ground.
Mire:	Blanket mire; lowland raised mire.	**Built:**	Built land.
Minund:	Wet ground; marginal inundation.		

Table 6

Changes of more than 10 square kilometres from one kind of feature to another in Cumbria between the 1940s and the 1970s, with estimates for the three broad land types

		Estimates in square kilometres			
		Upland	Intermediate	Lowland	County
Total area of land type within county (km²)		1969	2003	2717	6689
Change from	to				
Broadleaved woodland	Mixed woodland	0.3	2.2*	23.3	25.9
Broadleaved woodland	Scrub, low	1.6*	4.6*	9.6*	15.8*
Broadleaved woodland	Improved grassland	1.2	10.4*	11.4*	23.0*
Young plantation	Coniferous plantation	0.6	13.1	0.5	14.1
Scrub, low	Broadleaved woodland	0.6*	6.6*	14.2*	21.5*
Bracken	Unimproved grassland	7.9*	5.3	1.5	14.7*
Dwarf shrub heath, lowland	Broadleaved woodland	0.0	7.8	2.6	10.4
Dwarf shrub heath, lowland	Coniferous plantation	0.6	9.9	3.0	13.4*
Dwarf shrub heath, lowland	Unimproved grassland	5.9	9.9	0.4	16.2
Dwarf shrub heath, lowland	Semi-improved grassland	0.8	12.3	3.4*	16.5*
Dwarf shrub heath, moorland	Unimproved grassland	171.3*	19.8	1.4	192.5*
Blanket mire	Unimproved grassland	71.6*	2.7	0.0	74.3*
Unimproved grassland	Coniferous plantation	1.0	17.6*	5.0*	23.5*
Unimproved grassland	Scrub, low	5.6*	5.7*	13.0*	24.4*
Unimproved grassland	Bracken	22.9*	16.1*	25.1*	64.0*
Unimproved grassland	Semi-improved grassland	54.7*	51.4*	19.5*	125.5*
Unimproved grassland	Improved grassland	5.4	33.5*	32.9*	71.7*
Semi-improved grassland	Coniferous plantation	0.0	11.6	0.3	12.0
Semi-improved grassland	Unimproved grassland	8.5	13.0*	8.2*	29.7*
Semi-improved grassland	Improved grassland	12.1*	72.1*	60.7*	144.9*
Semi-improved grassland	Arable	0.8	2.8*	6.9*	10.4*
Improved grassland	Broadleaved woodland	0.5*	4.2*	5.4*	10.1*
Improved grassland	Scrub, low	0.8*	3.3*	8.7*	12.8*
Improved grassland	Semi-improved grassland	8.0*	35.6*	55.6*	99.2*
Improved grassland	Arable	2.9*	129.7*	274.6*	407.2*
Improved grassland	Built land	0.5	5.2*	38.2*	43.8*
Arable	Improved grassland	0.1	69.9*	212.6*	282.6*
Arable	Built land	0.0	0.5	10.3*	10.8*

Estimates are given to the nearest decimal place.

* Estimated with 95% confidence.

24

3.3   Linear feature estimates

Table 7 presents estimates of hedgerow and treeline lengths for the county. Over 9,000 kilometres of hedgerows have been lost since the 1940s. There have been smaller gains (3,434 km), and the percentage net loss for hedgerows varies across the land types from 38.3% in the Upland through 33.3% in the Intermediate to 21.9% in the Lowland.

Treelines are more limited in extent, and the net change has been relatively small, a loss of 7.7% for the county. This derives from a 25.1% gain and a 32.8% loss.

3.4   Reliability of the estimates

When interpreting these results it is necessary to take into account the standard errors associated with them. Net changes of 10% or more in extent were detected with 95% confidence in the county estimates for all the features indicated by an asterisk in Annex 1 (see Section 1.4) except coniferous plantation. The estimates for this feature were poor and the standard error large because it tends to occur in large isolated blocks; as a result, one sample square may be 90% coniferous plantation while the rest of the sample squares contain less than 5%.

The net change estimates for the grassland features over the whole county were less than 10%, or somewhat above in the case of semi-improved grassland (13.4%), but they were not detected with 95% confidence. All these features had large gains and losses which, when combined, gave small estimates of net change. The component gain and loss estimates were, however, detected with 95% confidence.

The estimates for each time period had similar standard errors to those for the estimates of change. Most of the estimates for the county at both periods were calculated with 95% confidence. An exception was standing natural water, because this feature occurs in large isolated blocks. None of the estimates totalling less than 5 km² were calculated with 95% confidence because of the small areas covered by these features. The estimates within each land type had larger standard errors because of the smaller samples. Linear features had very small standard errors because of their broad distribution.

The results for Cumbria demonstrate clearly the usefulness of stratification in reducing sample variability. For example, many of the features were found almost exclusively within only a few of the ITE's 16 land classes (see Section 2.1). Using these land classes as the basis for the stratification helped to explain much of the sample variability and in turn improved the accuracy of the estimates. Their use has also made it possible to reprocess the data obtained from the sample survey to provide estimates for the Lake District National Park.

4   Interpretation and discussion

The results indicate substantial changes in the Cumbrian countryside between the 1940s and the 1970s. Alterations in agricultural and forestry practice have clearly had a highly significant influence even in this north-western, 'upland' county where one might have expected considerable stability. The effects of the changes are discussed below in relation to the main features, particularly those of

Table 7

Estimates of hedgerow and treeline lengths in kilometres within each land type in the county of Cumbria

	Upland	Intermediate	Lowland	Total
Hedgerow				
1940s	267.0*	6359.8*	15480.6*	22107.4*
1970s	164.8*	4245.0*	12092.5*	16502.2*
Gains	49.8*	791.0*	2593.3*	3434.2*
Losses	152.1*	2905.8*	5981.5*	9039.4*
Net change	−102.3*	−2114.8*	−3388.2*	−5605.2*
Net change as a percentage of the length in the 1940s	−38.3*	−33.3*	−21.9*	−25.4*
Treeline				
1940s	134.0*	1002.2*	1437.9*	2574.1*
1970s	105.7*	901.1*	1370.1*	2376.9*
Gains	11.5*	262.0*	372.9*	646.4*
Losses	39.8*	363.2*	440.7*	843.6*
Net change	−28.3*	−101.2	−67.8	−197.2
Net change as a percentage of the length in the 1940s	−21.1*	−10.1	−4.7	−7.7
Hedgerow to treeline change	22.9	135.9*	159.0*	317.9*
Treeline to hedgerow change	8.5*	80.5*	106.7*	195.7*

Estimates are given to the nearest decimal place.

* Estimated with 95% confidence.

importance for nature conservation. In general, there is cause for concern about the effects that the extent and pace of these changes have had and may be having on the wildlife of the county. The semi-natural habitats that support Britain's diverse wildlife resource have developed with a continuity of management over many centuries. The rapid and dramatic changes associated with modern agricultural improvements and forestry practice have a catastrophic effect, as very few species can cope with them. The creation of new wildlife habitats, however laudable in itself, is a poor substitute for the retention of surviving sites of natural origin. For example, a plantation of native broadleaved trees in a new area will take very many years even to approach the level of species and structural diversity of a semi-natural woodland on a site which has never been cleared.

4.1 Woodland

In addition to the results of this study, a provisional inventory of ancient woodlands in Cumbria (NCC 1985) has been compiled, and it is useful to compare the results. The inventory estimates that 7.5% of the county area is woodland, with less than one-third thought to be ancient (2.3% of the county area). These figures accord well with those of this study, which suggest from the 1970s data (Table 1) that about 6% of the county is woodland, or 8% woodland and scrub. This study indicates an area of semi-natural broadleaved woodland equivalent to 2.8% of the county, but this is likely to include some broadleaved plantations (see Section 3.1).

The picture varies greatly around the county. Remaining semi-natural broadleaved woodland is most abundant in South Lakeland, particularly in the vicinity of the lakes of Windermere and Coniston Water. Otherwise its occurrence is scattered, and it has survived mainly along river valleys and in areas of steep ground and poor soil. The Solway Plain is an example of an area that is conspicuously poorly wooded.

The estimates of change (Table 1) are disturbing, particularly that nearly half (48%) of the semi-natural broadleaved woodland in the 1940s had been lost by the 1970s. The provisional inventory of ancient woodlands, which was based on different categories, definitions and time periods, estimates a loss of 36% of ancient semi-natural woodland (about 4% cleared, mainly for agriculture, and 32% changed to plantation). This is the woodland of the highest nature conservation importance, and a recruitment of other land to broadleaved woodland (equivalent to about 30% of the 1940s figure) is small recompense even though in purely landscape terms there may have been little obvious change. Losses between the 1940s and 1970s were approximately one-third to grassland, one-third to mixed and conifer woodland, and one-third to various other categories (see Table 5). A particular concern in Cumbria is the amount of semi-natural woodland used for stock-grazing. Clearly, unrestricted grazing over an extended period will prevent tree regeneration and cause a change to grassland.

The amount of coniferous afforestation has been difficult to define accurately in this study (see Section 3.4). However, the indications are of an increase of around 130%, mainly in the Intermediate land type (see Tables 1-4). The major plantings have been confined to existing plantations in the Lake District and to the Kershope Forest in the north of the county, but there have also been plantings on estates throughout the county.

4.2 Bracken

The changes recorded in the cover of bracken are noteworthy. An increase of 66% over the 30-year period is indicated (see Table 1), with the 1970s area of 165 km² coming close to the county area of semi-natural broadleaved woodland! Changes in agricultural grazing practice are implicated, but the resultant increase in bracken is of no benefit to the farmer or the conservationist. In fact, the loss of hill grassland to bracken (see Table 6) implies an even greater grazing pressure on the remaining open hill land.

4.3 Heath

Dwarf shrub heath of both the lowland and the moorland types is estimated to have decreased in area by 70% between the 1940s and the 1970s (see Table 1). This represents the most dramatic loss of wildlife habitat recorded by this study, and heathland, with its range of characteristic plants and variety of associated insects and birds, is an important wildlife habitat in Britain.

A proportion of the losses, particularly in the lowlands, is to plantation woodland, but the overwhelming change has been to grassland (see Tables 5 and 6). A separate investigation of one particular area where significant lowland heath remains, over the New Red Sandstone of the low fells north of Penrith, estimated heathland losses of over 65% in the last hundred years (P. Welsh, unpublished). Here the changes were divided equally between coniferous afforestation and agricultural conversion to improved grassland.

The upland dwarf shrub heaths appear to have undergone a more gradual degradation to unimproved grassland of less wildlife value. Presumably this has been caused largely by increased grazing pressure removing the dwarf shrubs.

4.4 Mire

Blanket mire is a major feature of the Pennine summits and accounts for 27% of the area of the Upland land type in Cumbria. It has shown a 12.5% loss between the 1940s and 1970s (see Tables 1-4). The change is almost entirely to unimproved grassland, presumably because drainage, burning and heavy grazing have converted the heather and cottongrass vegetation into a grass and rush sward. Further damage or loss of blanket mire would have serious consequences for the wildlife of Cumbria's moorland, especially its important breeding bird comunities.

Lowland raised mire is a particularly important wildlife resource in Cumbria, as the county retains three of the most valuable aggregations of such mire in Britain. The complex of raised mires in the Solway Plain, including Wedholme Flow, Bowness Common and Glasson Moss, is certainly the largest and most important, but the groupings in south Cumbria and east of Carlisle are also significant. This study estimates a loss over the 30-year period of about 19% of the raised mire, leaving a county area of 117 km² in the 1970s (see Table 1). However, these estimates are not likely to be very accurate, as lowland raised mire, like conifer plantation, occurs in large irregularly dispersed blocks (see Section 3.4). It is instructive to compare the results of a separate more detailed study of change in the most important Solway and south Cumbria raised mires. This investigated changes between 1948 and 1978 and indicated a loss of 40%, with only 9.5 km² remaining (NCC 1984). The major losses noted in that study were to bare peat (a category not included in the present study) or scrub, as a result of peat extraction, and to improved grassland.

4.5   Grassland

The changes recorded for grassland are complex and rather difficult to interpret because of problems in clearly distinguishing the categories. For example, herb-rich hay meadows or pastures might appear in aerial photographs as being intensively managed, showing cutting or harrowing lines. Consequently, this floristically rich grassland could possibly be recorded within the semi-improved or improved grassland categories, even with some field checking. What can be distinguished with more certainty in the unimproved and semi-improved groupings is the amount of open hill grassland and of rough and often wet and rushy grassland of hill and lowland.

Net changes in the grassland categories are small for the county as a whole, not because the situation was static but rather because the considerable gains and losses over the period balanced out (see Section 3.1 and Table 1). In the case of improved grassland, much of the interchange can be explained by the normal rotation between grassland and arable. As with other habitats, more permanent changes invariably meant a decrease in nature conservation value. For example, much of the gain in unimproved grassland was at the expense of heath and blanket mire (see Table 6).

Perhaps the most important change to note (see Tables 1 and 5) was the 26.5% loss of the unimproved grassland present in the 1940s, and the most dramatic component of this was a 65.5% gross loss (48.5% net loss) in the Lowland land type (see Table 2). This grassland would have been valuable in botanical terms as well as in supporting insect communities and such breeding birds as snipe, curlew and lapwing. The change (see Tables 5 and 6) has been mainly to semi-improved or improved grassland (56%), but also to bracken (18%), conifer (9%) and scrub (8%).

4.6   Built land

Of particular significance are the estimated 222 km^2 of built land in Cumbria in the 1970s, an increase of 43% over the 1940s, developed mostly over improved grassland or arable (see Tables 1 and 5) and resulting in an area greater than that occupied by semi-natural broadleaved woodland!

4.7   Linear features

Hedgerows have undergone considerable change even in this relatively unintensive agricultural county (see Table 7). Over the 30-year period there was a 41% gross (25% net) loss in hedgerow length. The smaller gains in hedgerows provide little compensation for these losses because the quality of these new hedgerows as wildlife habitats is much less than that of the older ones. Treelines are less extensive generally but have also shown a large gross loss (33%), though only an 8% net loss. Much of the gain in treelines appears to derive from hedgerows that have been left unmanaged.

Appendix Technical aspects of the project methods

1 Differences in the completeness of aerial photographic cover

The choice of aerial photography was a constraint imposed by the requirements of the study for complete or nearly complete cover: this is only available as black and white panchromatic prints. The most comprehensive cover is at a smaller scale (approximately 1:25,000 rather than 1:10,000). Incomplete cover is subject to unknown bias, though the method of weighting the estimates according to the relative abundance of land types and classes within the county reduces this effect.

The scale of the photography must not be too small, or it is impossible to interpret the features listed in Annex 1, but the larger the scale the greater is the time needed to collect the data. For example, it could take 16 times as long to map a 5 x 5 km square using 1:10,000 scale photography as it does when using 1:25,000 scale photography. It has thus been necessary to make a compromise and use aerial photography at a scale of 1:25,000.

2 Sample size

The main determinant of sampling intensity is the sampling variance. Until estimates of sampling variance had been obtained from a few counties in the present project, the best initial guide to the required sampling intensity was a study of lowland agricultural habitats in Scotland (Langdale-Brown et al. 1980), in which the criterion of significant change was the same as in the present project, namely that changes of 10% in the extent of features should be detected with 95% statistical confidence. In the Scottish study it was found that a 10% sample satisfied this requirement.

3 Differences in exact dates of air-photo cover

The two time periods for sampling in Cumbria were the end of the 1940s and the beginning of the 1970s, two periods when almost complete air-photo cover exists for Great Britain. Whenever possible, photography was selected within two years of each mean survey date (1947 and 1973). Where this is not possible, the estimates of change between the two periods can be standardised by calculating annual rates of change. In fact, this proved an unnecessary refinement for the Cumbria study, but it may prove necessary when one county is compared with another.

4 Mechanics of sampling

The sampling frame for each county (or district) is based on the Ordnance Survey's National Grid, so that the results can readily be matched to other information. At a scale of 1:25,000, one air-photo covers approximately 25 square kilometres. Sampling is therefore from 5 x 5 km squares of the National Grid. The use of the grid prevents independently selected sample sites from overlapping. Although the basic sampling units are 5 x 5 km squares, data are recorded from every possible 1 x 1 km square within each sampling unit, so that estimates of extent and change of features can be made for these smaller land units. For Cumbria, the 5 x 5 km and 1 x 1 km squares were both stratified into the Upland, Intermediate and Lowland land types, as described in Section 2.1. Samples were obtained from a list of all candidate units in the county, thus giving equal probability of selection to each unit irrespective of its size: undersized units (such as along the county boundary or in coastal areas) were thus selected on an equal footing with central units. The objective was to provide approximately equal numbers of units from each of the three land types.

Even if one land type covers a much smaller proportion of a county than the other two, approximately equal numbers of units are still selected from each type by continuing the sampling until the required number for the smallest type is reached and by ignoring superfluous units selected from the larger types.

Figure 5 illustrates the procedures used when sampling at two time periods. Air-photo cover is shown for one sample 5 x 5 km square at two dates (T1 and T2). The stereoscopic cover at T1 is approximately 50%, and at T2 approximately 85%. Within each 5 x 5 km square, data are collected only from whole or parts of 1 km squares having stereoscopic cover both for T1 and for T2.

5   Air-photo quality

The quality of the photography is an important factor that must be taken into account. If the quality is poor, mapping and interpretation are virtually impossible regardless of the scale of the photographs. It is thus important to ensure that the photography for both periods is of sufficiently good quality.

6   Sources of aerial photographs

After defining the requirements for the aerial photography, the problem is to find the photographs that achieve them. There are three major sources of air-photos in Britain - the Ordnance Survey, the Royal Air Force and the County and Regional Councils. Photography from other sources is usually limited in extent and thus likely to be of little use for projects such as this.

7   Air-photo interpretation

The interpretation of the aerial photographs is fundamental to accurate measurement. Thus considerable time has been spent in developing the interpretation techniques. The usefulness of black and white photographs for interpretation is limited because they represent colour as various shades of grey. The interpreter must thus be very familiar with the features involved on the ground, and it is helpful if he or she also has some knowledge of farming practice, particularly for interpreting the early photographs.

Seasonal effects are very important when interpreting aerial photographs. How the features appear on the photographs can vary considerably according to the season. Some seasons are better for identifying particular features than others (see Section 2.3).

A detailed key has been developed to aid photo-interpretation as a result of the experience gained in the Cumbria survey. The prime aim of the key is to lay down strict criteria for identifying features, to help to achieve consistency in interpretation.

Even if there is complete air-photo cover, this does not mean that the whole of each photograph can be used for data collection. There are several reasons why parts of the photograph may be obscured. These include military installations, which are blanked out for security purposes; cloud cover, which can obscure parts

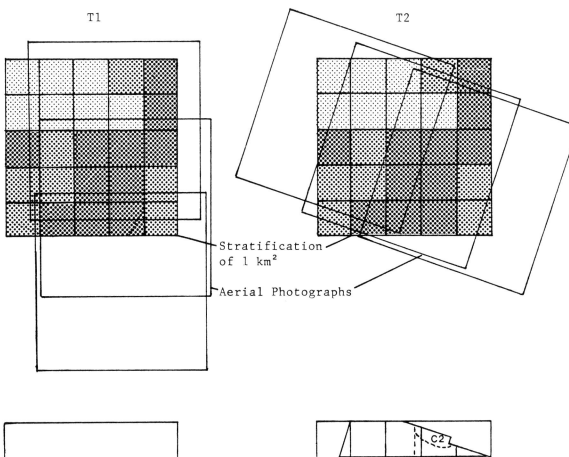

Stereo cover within
sample square at T1

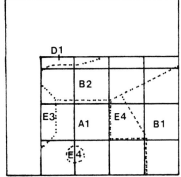

Stereo cover within
sample square at T2

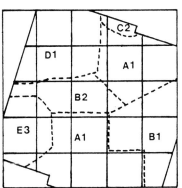

Overlap between stereo
cover at T1 and T2

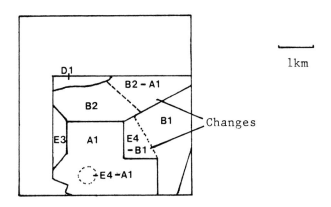

Figure 5   Diagrams of aerial photographic cover of a sample 5 x 5 km square of the National Grid available at two time periods (T1 and T2), showing selection of 1 km squares with stereoscopic cover for both T1 and T2

of the ground below; shadow created by cloud or topography, which can severely restrict the available information; and snow cover, which makes most features unrecognisable. Shadow and snow cover may consistently or frequently obscure certain kinds of features; for example, shadow may cause problems below cliffs, and upland habitats are the most likely to be covered by snow. It is thus important to limit these factors as far as possible, and this may involve additional fieldwork. If these problems cannot be resolved, the areas have to be treated as if there is no air-photo cover.

8   The photogrammetric plotting machine

It was decided to use a photogrammetric plotting machine (Kern PG2-L) for the interpretation and mapping work as these can be done as one process on it, thus saving time. This machine is designed to produce paper maps, using the pantograph and plotting table attached. However, in order to automate the process of area and length measurement the machine has been modified so that the mapped data can be recorded as three digital co-ordinates. Two of these describe the boundaries of the features while the third records their altitude by reference to known spot heights. This allows the estimates for particular kinds of features to be related to altitude. The digital data are stored in a computer and can then be used to calculate areas and lengths of features. It is also possible to compare two sets of data to identify the changes in area and length. Finally, the computer is used to prepare the results for use in the statistical programs.

Acknowledgements

We are grateful to the staff of the Unit of Statistics of the Agricultural and Food Research Council at the University of Edinburgh for their help with the project, and in particular to Dr Chris Kershaw, who designed and created the statistical software for the analysis of the data. Thanks are also due to Mr George Jolly, who designed the sampling and statistical procedures used in the project.

The Cumbria data were assembled with the use of the Kern PG2-L photogrammetric plotting machine in the Geography Department of Portsmouth Polytechnic while the NCC's machine was in transit. The Forestry Commission loaned its digital mapping system for use with the PG2 and also for the analysis of the data. Without the use of this equipment the project would have been delayed many months.

References

ANDERSON, H.L., & BUDD, J.T.C. 1984. Aerial cover of Cumbria, 1945-1983. (NCC Chief Scientist Directorate internal report).

BUNCE, R.G.H., & SMITH, R.S. 1978. An ecological survey of Cumbria. Kendal, Cumbria County Council and Lake District Special Planning Board.

COCHRAN, W.G. 1977. Sampling techniques. 3rd ed. London, Wiley. (Chapter 6).

LANGDALE-BROWN, I., JENNINGS, S., CRAWFORD, C.L., JOLLY, G.M., & MUSCOTT, J. 1980. Lowland agricultural habitats (Scotland): air-photo analysis of change. Peterborough, Nature Conservancy Council. (CST report no. 332).

NATURE CONSERVANCY COUNCIL. 1984. Nature conservation in Great Britain.

NATURE CONSERVANCY COUNCIL. 1985. Cumbria inventory of ancient woodlands (Provisional). (Report prepared for NCC Chief Scientist Directorate by A. Whitbread).

Annex 1　List of features to be recorded

Group A	Group B

*Hedgerow (including hedgerow with trees):
                Hedgerow without trees
                Treeline, including hedgerow with trees

Woodland:
                *Semi-natural broadleaved woodland
                Broadleaved plantation
                Semi-natural coniferous woodland
                *Coniferous plantation
                Semi-natural mixed woodland
                Mixed plantation
                Young plantation
                Recently felled woodland

Parkland

*Scrub:
                Scrub, tall
                Scrub, low

Bracken

*Heathland:
                Dwarf shrub heath, lowland
                *Dwarf shrub heath, moorland

Mire:
                *Blanket mire
                Lowland raised mire

Wet ground

Marginal inundation

*Open water:
                Standing natural water
                Standing man-made water
                Running natural water
                Running canalised water

Grassland:
                *Unimproved grassland
                Semi-improved grassland
                *Improved grassland

*Arable

*Bare rock and soil:
                Unquarried inland cliff and outcrop
                Quarries and open-cast mines, including spoil
                Other bare ground

*Built land

*Habitats where 10% net change is estimated with 95% confidence.

Annex 2   Definitions of features

Hedgerow:
Less than 4 m high. Classified as continuous if gaps are less than 10 m wide. Maximum width is 5 m.

Treeline:
Line of single trees (minimum of three) greater than 4 m high and less than two canopy widths apart. Hedges may be associated with treelines.

Semi-natural broadleaved woodland:
More than 50% broadleaved woodland with a tree height more than 5 m, with semi-natural/natural growth.

Broadleaved plantation:
More than 50% planted broadleaved trees. Species not native to the site and of even age.

Semi-natural coniferous woodland:
More than 50% coniferous woodland of any height, with semi-natural/natural growth.

Coniferous plantation:
More than 50% coniferous trees which have been planted.

Semi-natural mixed woodland:
More than 25% broadleaved and more than 25% coniferous woodland with semi-natural/natural growth. Trees more than 5 m tall. Planted trees less than 25% of canopy cover.

Mixed plantation:
More than 25% broadleaved and more than 25% coniferous woodland, planted. If the blocks or lines of coniferous or broadleaved trees exceed two trees in width they are recorded as coniferous or broadleaved plantation.

Young plantation:
Young trees both coniferous and broadleaved which have been planted. Height of trees up to 3 m.

Recently felled woodland:
Area for which there is evidence that woodland has been felled recently. At least 50% of woodland felled.

Parkland:
Majority of trees separated by at least one canopy width (30 m) and less than 70 m. Minimum of two trees per hectare. Minimum number of trees ten. Includes coniferous and broadleaved trees. Tree cover must be less than 30%.

Scrub, tall:
Between 3 and 5 m in height and can have a closed canopy. Stands less than 5 m tall are classified as woodland rather than scrub when composed mostly of tree species (i.e. more than 50% immature canopy cover).

Scrub, low:
No distinct canopy and vegetation less than 3 m tall.

Bracken:
Land dominated by bracken with at least 75% cover.

Dwarf shrub heath, lowland:
Lowland areas with more than 25% dwarf shrubs. Burnt patches are included as dwarf shrub heath if there is sufficient evidence that they will regenerate.

Dwarf shrub heath, moorland:
As last but on upland sites.

Blanket mire:
Peat to a depth of more than 0.5 m.

Lowland raised mire:
More than 0.5 m of peat formed into a shallow dome of ombrotrophic bog.

Wet ground:
This classification covers areas of wet land found in association with other habitats, for example wet areas in a grassland field or flushes in upland areas.

Marginal inundation:
Swamp and fen, excluding coastal marsh. Also includes areas of regular inundation.

Standing natural water:
No evidence of damming.

Standing man-made water:
Reservoirs and impoundments which have been artificially created.

Running natural water:
No evidence of canalisation.

Running canalised water:
A watercourse that has been confined to flow in a certain direction by man.

Unimproved grassland:
Regularly grazed or mown but may be neglected. It may be treated with a farm manure, but has not been improved by the application of fertilisers or herbicides so as significantly to alter the sward composition.

Semi-improved grassland:
Includes those fields or areas of grassland which have been slightly modified by fertiliser or herbicide application or perhaps by heavy grazing pressure and/or drainage.

Improved grassland:
Grassland that has had regular treatment of artificial fertilisers and/or herbicides and has been reseeded. It does not include monoculture grassland, i.e. grassland ley.

Arable:
All classes of arable including grassland ley and horticulture.

Unquarried inland cliff and outcrop:
Unvegetated rock (or other mineral substrate) over 5 m in height and at an angle of at least 60°. Includes scree.

Quarries and open-cast mines:
Any excavation (i.e. gravel pits, chalk pits etc). Includes unvegetated spoil heaps.

Other bare ground:
Bare soil or ground that is not covered by vegetation and does not fall into the two previous definitions.

Built land:
Any urban area, including gardens, parks, golf courses and transport corridors. Individual buildings are recorded outside urban areas.

Supplement   Rates of change in features of the Cumbrian countryside since the 1970s

Aerial photographic coverage for Cumbria during the 1980s was known to be insufficient for the requirements of this study as outlined in Chapter 1. Hence the study assessed changes between about 1947 and 1973 (see Section 2.2 and Appendix, Section 3). However, when the analysis was complete, it was decided that an attempt should be made to assess whether the changes had continued in the 1980s.

Air photographs taken in 1983-1985 were located for ten of the 5 x 5 km squares used in the main study. (These included the 1983 MAFF photographs referred to in Section 2.2.) As these squares represented only about one-third of the original sample squares used for the comparison between the 1940s and the 1970s, coverage was inadequate for full comparisons to be made between the 1940s and the 1980s or the 1970s and the 1980s. The photographs were, however, judged to be adequate for estimating average annual rates of change for some of the principal features.

Thus, the aim of this supplementary study was not to determine absolute values but to ascertain whether the pace of change in the Cumbrian countryside had accelerated, declined or remained substantially the same.

In general, the results obtained suggest that the trends observed in the main study have continued. Table 8 shows the estimated annual percentage rates of change for some of the principal features. These reveal rates of change over the last decade remarkably similar to those observed in the period of the main study.

Table 8

Estimated annual percentage rates of change in selected features in Cumbria

	From 1940s to 1970s	From 1970s to 1980s
Semi-natural broadleaved woodland	– 0.5%	– 0.6%
Coniferous plantation	+ 4.2%	+ 3.5%
Unimproved grassland	+ 0.1%	– 0.1%
Dwarf shrub heath	– 2.3%	0.0%
Built land	+ 1.4%	+ 1.4%
Hedgerows	– 0.8%	– 0.5%